A cartoonist is someone who has to draw the same thing day after day without repeating himself.

Sometimes there are days when ideas come very rapidly, but unfortunately, there are also days when nothing comes at all, and no matter how hard I try to draw something meaningful, something to touch the hearts of everyone, I find it impossible.

At times like these, I never stop trying. I sit at my drawing board and make up little conversations with myself, searching my past for ideas, drawing Snoopy and the others in different poses, hoping something new will come along.

One solution I use when everything else fails is simply to get back to basics. Cartooning is, after all, drawing funny pictures, something a cartoonist should never forget. If a cartoonist remains within his own medium, if he does not let himself become carried too far afield and always remembers that his business is to draw funny pictures, then I believe he will have a minimum of bad days.

I am not concerned with simply surviving. I am very concerned about improving. I start each day by examining yesterday's work and looking for areas where I can improve . . .

To have staying power you must be willing to accommodate yourself to the task. I have never maintained that a comic strip is Great Art. It simply happens to be something I feel uniquely qualified to do.

Charles M. Schulz

THE 1991 · · ·
Snoopy
ANNUAL

Created by
CHARLES M. SCHULZ

Written by
Gordon Volke

ℛ
RAVETTE BOOKS

Contents

Published by
Ravette Books Limited 1990

Printed and bound for
Ravette Books Limited,
3 Glenside Estate,
Star Road, Partridge Green,
Horsham, West Sussex RH13 8RA
by BPCC Paulton Books Limited

ISBN 1 85304 277 3

Anyone for Tennis?

Snoopy had been watching Wimbledon on TV. It was a very exciting match and afterwards Snoopy felt like playing tennis himself. So he put on his special tennis cap, fetched his racket and hurried outside. "Who am I going to play with?" he wondered.

Snoopy's usual partners, Molly Volley and Bad Call Benny, were on a tennis-coaching course. Peppermint Patty, the other keen athlete amongst Snoopy's friends, was away at Summer Camp with Marcie, and most of his other friends had gone to the seaside for the day. "I could ask Sally," thought Snoopy, "but she's not a very good player, and Charlie Brown's too busy dreaming about The Little Red-Haired Girl. So who is there?"

Just then, a familiar figure flew down and perched on Snoopy's kennel. "!!!" squawked Woodstock. "You?" exclaimed Snoopy. "I can't play tennis with you!" Woodstock hung his head and assumed a hurt expression. "Listen, my little friend," continued Snoopy, "it's not that I don't *want* to play tennis with you. It's just that I *can't* play tennis with you because you're too *small!* You couldn't even hold the racket, for one thing."

BOOT!

BOOT!

BOOT!

Now Woodstock looked really upset, so Snoopy gave his best friend a cuddle. "Remember what happened when you tried to play golf?" he said. "You fell down the hole! And when you played basketball? You perched on the basket and the ball flattened you! Worst of all, what about the time you attempted to play American Football?" "!!!" spluttered Woodstock. "All right," agreed Snoopy, "we won't say any more about it." By now, Woodstock was convinced that he was not big enough to play tennis with Snoopy. So he flew off and perched sadly on a nearby tree. "I still haven't got anyone to play with!" sighed Snoopy.

Snoopy set off for the park. When he got there, he did what every other partnerless tennis player has done since time immemorial – he found himself a wall! Having chalked a thin line across it about net-height, he prepared to play alone. "Stand by, wall," he warned, "you're about to be blasted by the best forehand in the game." Snoopy bounced the ball and swung his racket back ready to hit it. "Hang on, Snoopy," called Charlie Brown, "I'll play tennis with you!"

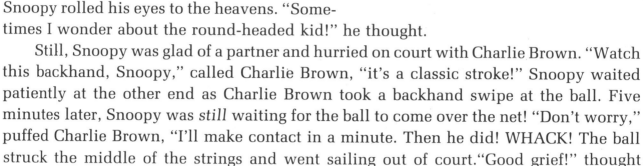

Charlie Brown had grown tired of dreaming about The Little Red-Haired Girl. "Yesterday, in the advice booth, Lucy told me to search for 'realistic goals'," explained Charlie Brown, "so I'm really looking for a game of soccer. But as it's not the season, tennis will do instead!" Snoopy rolled his eyes to the heavens. "Sometimes I wonder about the round-headed kid!" he thought.

Still, Snoopy was glad of a partner and hurried on court with Charlie Brown. "Watch this backhand, Snoopy," called Charlie Brown, "it's a classic stroke!" Snoopy waited patiently at the other end as Charlie Brown took a backhand swipe at the ball. Five minutes later, Snoopy was *still* waiting for the ball to come over the net! "Don't worry," puffed Charlie Brown, "I'll make contact in a minute. Then he did! WHACK! The ball struck the middle of the strings and went sailing out of court. "Good grief!" thought Snoopy.

Snoopy spent the next half-an-hour searching the bushes for the ball. At last he found it and returned it to Charlie Brown who promptly proceeded to hit it out of court again! "I've had enough of this!" thought Snoopy. Then the clever beagle had an idea. He put his paws in his mouth and emitted an ear-piercing whistle. A few moments later, Woodstock flew down and perched on the net.

Snoopy went up and spoke to his tiny friend. "You know you wanted to join in the game," he grinned. "Well, now's your chance. We need someone to fetch the ball. You can be our Ball-Bird!"

Woodstock was delighted with his new job. He scurried backwards and forwards across the court, fetching every ball that Charlie Brown hit or mis-hit. Snoopy watched happily from the other end. "Woodstock feels important now that he's busy," he thought to himself.

In fact, Woodstock was a little *too* busy! Before very long, the tiny bird felt exhausted! He sat down in a corner of the court, panting and sweating. Snoopy picked Woodstock up and carried him to a nearby fountain for a reviving drink. "Sorry!" he said. "At Wimbledon, they change the ball-boys every so often. We should have done the same."

When he was satisfied that Woodstock felt better, Snoopy returned to the game. "We've been playing for half an hour now," he thought, "and I still haven't hit the ball!" So Snoopy prepared to serve. To make it look professional, Snoopy bounced the ball in front of him over and over again. "Get on with it!" called Charlie Brown, impatiently. "Doesn't he know you can't hurry an ace!" thought Snoopy.

Eventually, Snoopy tossed the ball into the air and prepared to strike it. "Hold it!" called an urgent voice. "Can I play?"

It was Lucy. She was feeling even more crabby than usual. "I've been stuck indoors, helping with the housework," she explained, marching onto court, "so I'm desperate for some fresh air and exercise."

"But we've only got two rackets," said Charlie Brown.

"That's all right," exclaimed Lucy, snatching Charlie Brown's racket from his hand, "I'll borrow yours!"

"You can't do that!" protested Charlie Brown.

"Yes, I can!" retorted Lucy.

"No, you can't!"

"Can!"

"Can't!"

"WAAH!" yelled Lucy.

As usual, Charlie Brown gave in and let Lucy have her way. "I'll nip home and fetch another racket," he called. "There's a spare one in the shed."

Lucy hit the ball to Snoopy. "Hurray!" thought Snoopy, knocking it back, "a game of tennis at last." "OUT!" shouted Lucy. "What did she say?" wondered Snoopy. "That ball was in by a mile!" Snoopy marched round the net and pointed at the spot where the ball had bounced. "It wasn't there," snapped Lucy, pointing to another spot beyond the baseline, "it was here!" Snoopy shook his head. "Are you arguing with me? snorted Lucy. Snoopy nodded.

"WAAH!" yelled Lucy.

"Good grief!" thought Snoopy, again.

Lucy refused to play any more tennis unless they had an umpire. "And I don't know where we're going to find one either," she added. Snoopy knew. He hurried out of court and beckoned to Woodstock who was sitting on a nearby tree. "Another job for you," he smiled.

Woodstock was made the umpire. He perched on the ground by the net and gave one squawk if the ball was in and two squawks if it went out. At first, the system worked well and Umpire Woodstock controlled the game perfectly. Then came a ball he could not see and the arguments began again. "Woodstock's too low down there," thought Snoopy, "he needs to be up higher." Short of hovering in the air,

there was nowhere for the little bird to perch – until Snoopy had a brilliant idea. Winking at Lucy, the brainy beagle marched off court once more.

Snoopy scampered round to Lucy's house in search of her little brother, Rerun. He was just setting off for the shops on the back of his mother's bike.

Snoopy waved and pointed to Rerun's high-chair which was standing in the conservatory. "Of course you can borrow it,

Snoopy," called Rerun. "I don't use it now. I'm a big boy, Mum says!" Snoopy grinned and staggered back to the tennis court with the high-chair on his back. Then he ran off to Charlie Brown's house to fetch a drinks-dispenser. "If you're going to do something," thought Snoopy, "you have to do it properly!"

Snoopy placed Woodstock on top of the high-chair. Then he placed the drinks-dispenser on the shelf in the middle. "WOW!" exclaimed Lucy. "A real umpire's chair – just like at Wimbledon."

A few moments later, Charlie Brown returned with two more rackets and a bag of extra tennis balls. They belonged to Peppermint Patty who was walking beside him. "I came home early from Summer Camp," she explained. "It was raining up in the mountains and we had to stay indoors, doing projects. You know how much I like schoolwork!"

Now there were enough players for a game of mixed doubles. And there was an umpire who could see all of the court – plus a big dispenser of orange juice for drinks at changeover time. Snoopy felt so excited that he sent a series of blistering forehands over the net.

"Good grief!" exclaimed the others.

"At last," thought Snoopy, happily, "JOE WIMBLEDON!"

The world has changed enormously since Snoopy made his first appearance in October 1950. He has many memories of the special events, happy moments and fads and fashions that have come and gone during the past four decades. Snoopy has kept his memories alive with the help of a scrapbook which is about to be opened for the first time . . .

THE FIFTIES

M1 OPENS

Britain's first motorway, the M1, opened in 1959. Drivers had to be instructed in the techniques of motorway driving.

Picturepoint – London

Rock 'n' roll burst on the scene in 1956 in the person of Elvis Presley. The new music was taken up in Britain by Cliff Richard, Tommy Steele and Marty Wilde. Many people viewed rock with mistrust, but teenagers loved it. They agreed with Bill Hayley (singer of 'Rock Around The Clock') when he said: "Don't knock the rock!"

Royal Geographical Society / Picturepoint

In 1953, Sir Edmund Hillary and his guide, Sherpa Tensing, became the first men to reach the summit of Mount Everest.

ANIMALS IN SPACE

The first living creatures to go into Space were animals. During the 1950s, the Russians and Americans launched satellites containing mice, dogs and monkeys which orbited the Earth.

FIFTIES FASHIONS

Fashions followed the new trend in pop music. Teddy Boys used lots of grease on their hair and wore drainpipe trousers and crepe-soled shoes. Girls had buffon hairstyles and wore wide skirts with lots of petticoats underneath. The jive was the 'in' dance.

Picturepoint – London

Queen Elizabeth The Second was crowned in 1953. For the first time, the Coronation was witnessed by millions of people, thanks to the miracle of television. Many people bought their first TV set just to watch the ceremony.

Picturepoint – London

In 1958 and 1959, hula-hoops were all the rage, especially amongst girls. Boys preferred wearing Davy Crockett-style coonskin caps.

ITV LAUNCHED

Britain's second television channel went on the air in 1955. Unlike the BBC, the new ITV channel broadcast adverts between its programmes.

There's more nostalgia with Peanuts from the 1950s on the next 5 pages . . .

PEANUTS

By Schulz

1950

PEANUTS

By Schulz

1951

1955

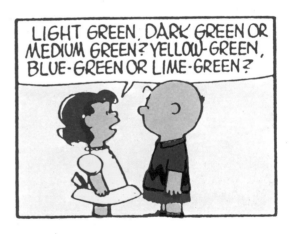

1956

BEAUTIFUL BEAGLES

'The beagle is a merry, affectionate fellow, loving humans, other dogs and animals alike. You won't have to teach your beagle to like children. He will be mad about them. The beagle is a wonderful companion and the most intelligent of the hounds. Their main wish is to please their friends. So if you're looking for a real pal, you don't have to look any further.'

The Beagle Club

The beagle is an ancient breed of dog. Records show that it was known over 2000 years ago in Ancient Greece.

In Britain, the poet Geoffrey Chaucer (1340-1400) was the first to mention beagles. In the 'Canterbury Tales', he calls them 'smale houndes'. The name 'beagle' was first coined in 1475.

Beagles were originally hunting dogs. Queen Elizabeth The First kept a pack, as did King George The Fourth.

Beagles come in a variety of colours. The most common combination is known as 'the tricolour' – a mixture of black, white and tan.

The Pocket Beagle is a special miniature breed which is only about 25 cm tall when fully grown. The breed is now so rare that it is virtually extinct.

Nowadays, beagles are mainly kept singly, as pets. Over 1000 thoroughbred dogs are registered every year, making the beagle one of the country's most popular breeds.

Beagles don't bark like other dogs, but they do bay loudly, especially when chasing something.

The beagle is well-known for its short coat which is tough, waterproof and needs no grooming. The breed also has a reputation for being lively, healthy and robust.

THE PERFECT BEAGLE

SHOULD HAVE . . .

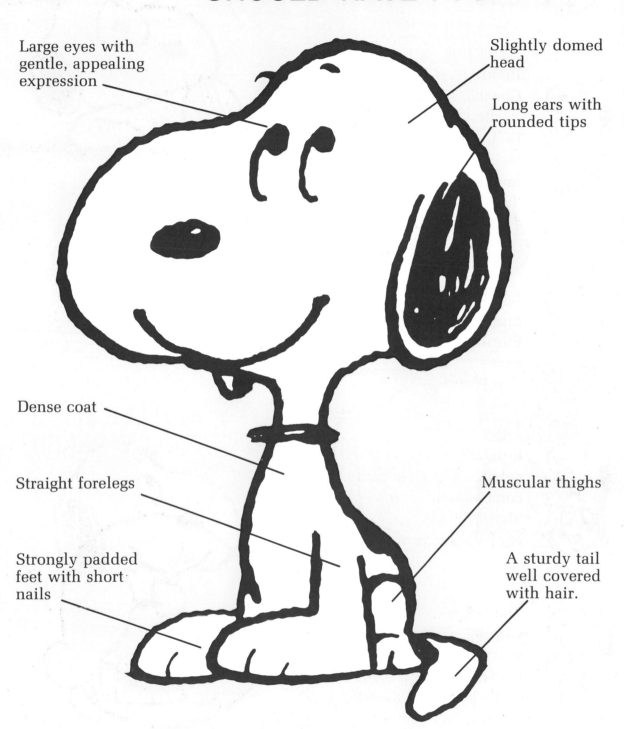

Large eyes with gentle, appealing expression

Slightly domed head

Long ears with rounded tips

Dense coat

Straight forelegs

Muscular thighs

Strongly padded feet with short nails

A sturdy tail well covered with hair.

Information and photographs kindly supplied by The Beagle Club.

LAUGHTER IS THE BEST MEDICINE – UNLESS IT'S AT YOUR EXPENSE!

NOTHING TASTES BETTER THAN WATER FROM A DRINKING FOUNTAIN!

(BUT YOU HAVE TO FIND ONE THAT WORKS!)

"IT'S WARMER ONCE YOU GET IN" MEANS THE WATER'S ABSOLUTELY FREEZING!

THE SIXTIES

Picturepoint – London

The Sixties are synonymous with The Beatles. They began as 'loveable mop-tops', singing to hordes of screaming fans at huge concerts in Britain and America, As the decade progressed, they changed their image and their music which became more complex and psychedelic. Their masterpiece, 'Sergeant Pepper's Lonely Hearts Club Band', was released in 1967.

Picturepoint – London

FOLK BOOM

The early Sixties also saw folk music reaching a mass audience. Traditional songs were made commercial by groups such as the Kingston Trio and Peter, Paul and Mary. Others, like Bob Dylan, Joan Baez and Phil Ochs, wrote and sang modern folk songs.

In 1969, Neil Armstrong became the first man to set foot on the surface of the Moon.

Picturepoint – London

The Mini-skirt was the other famous symbol of 'The Swinging Sixties'. This one is being worn in Carnaby Street, the centre of pop fashion at the time.

'THE GREATEST'

Cassius Clay (now known as Muhammed Ali) was world heavyweight boxing champion from 1964-67. One of the most famous fighters of all time, Clay outraged his opponents by predicting the round in which they would lose. He had two catchphrases: 'Float like a butterfly, sting like a bee' and 'I am the greatest!'

FAMOUS FASHIONS

Mods – wore narrow suits, parka anoraks trimmed with fur and rode motor-scooters. (Early 60s)

Rockers – wore leather gear and rode motor-bikes. (Early 60s)

Hippies – wore beads, fringes and long hair. Sometimes known as The Flower People. (Middle to late 60s)

THE OTHER MINI

The car of the decade was the BMC Mini (which is still produced today). Designed by Sir Alec Issigonis and launched in 1959, the millionth Mini rolled out of the factory in 1965.

Picturepoint – London

In 1966, England won the World Cup. In a thrilling final at Wembley, they beat West Germany 4-2 in a match that went into extra time.

1960

I GUESS SOMEBODY'S GETTING HUNGRY!

1964

PEANUTS

THIS IS A STEEP HILL, SNOOPY..

BUT WE'RE NOT AFRAID, ARE WE?

WE KNOW THAT NO MATTER WHAT DANGERS LIE AHEAD, WE CAN FACE THEM IF WE STICK TOGETHER..

1-22

1965

11-10

FEELIN' GROOVY!

PEANUTS

It was a dark and stormy night.

8-28

YOUR NEW NOVEL HAS A VERY EXCITING BEGINNING..

THANK YOU

GOOD LUCK WITH THE SECOND SENTENCE!

1969

PEANUTS

THAT LITTLE RED-HAIRED GIRL IS GOING TO MOVE AWAY!

7-16

I'VE NEVER EVEN TALKED TO HER! I THOUGHT I HAD PLENTY OF TIME... I THOUGHT I COULD WAIT UNTIL THE SIXTH-GRADE SWIM PARTY OR THE SEVENTH-GRADE CLASS PARTY...

OR I THOUGHT I COULD ASK HER TO THE SENIOR PROM OR LOTS OF OTHER THINGS WHEN WE GOT OLDER, BUT NOW SHE'S MOVING AWAY AND IT'S TOO LATE! IT'S TOO LATE!

YOU'VE GOT TO SAY GOODBY TO HER, CHARLIE BROWN!

I'VE NEVER EVEN SAID **HELLO** TO HER!!

SNOOPY'S CIRCLE OF FRIENDS

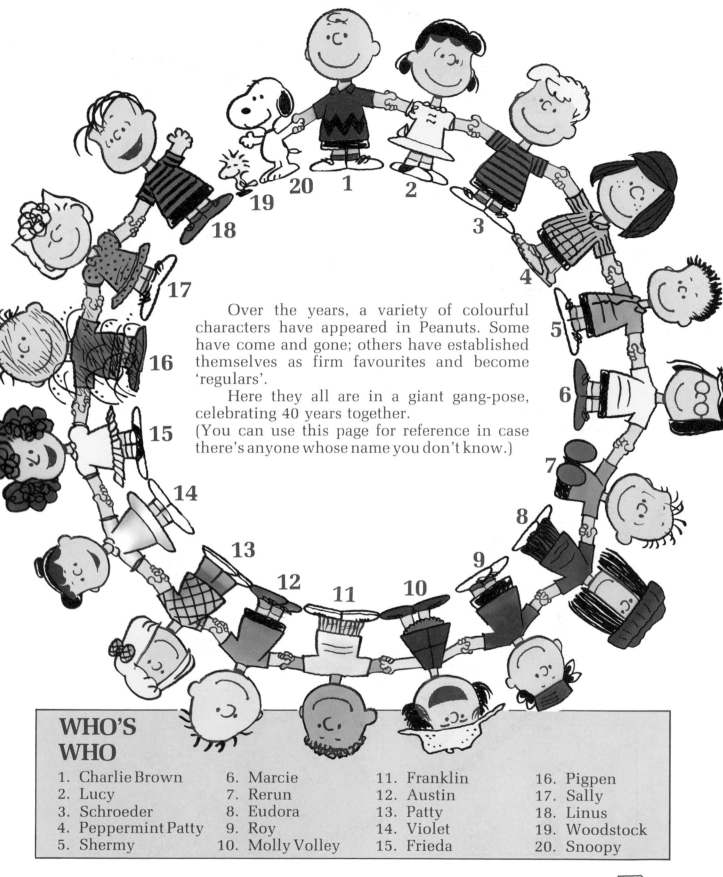

Over the years, a variety of colourful characters have appeared in Peanuts. Some have come and gone; others have established themselves as firm favourites and become 'regulars'.

Here they all are in a giant gang-pose, celebrating 40 years together.

(You can use this page for reference in case there's anyone whose name you don't know.)

WHO'S WHO

1. Charlie Brown
2. Lucy
3. Schroeder
4. Peppermint Patty
5. Shermy
6. Marcie
7. Rerun
8. Eudora
9. Roy
10. Molly Volley
11. Franklin
12. Austin
13. Patty
14. Violet
15. Frieda
16. Pigpen
17. Sally
18. Linus
19. Woodstock
20. Snoopy

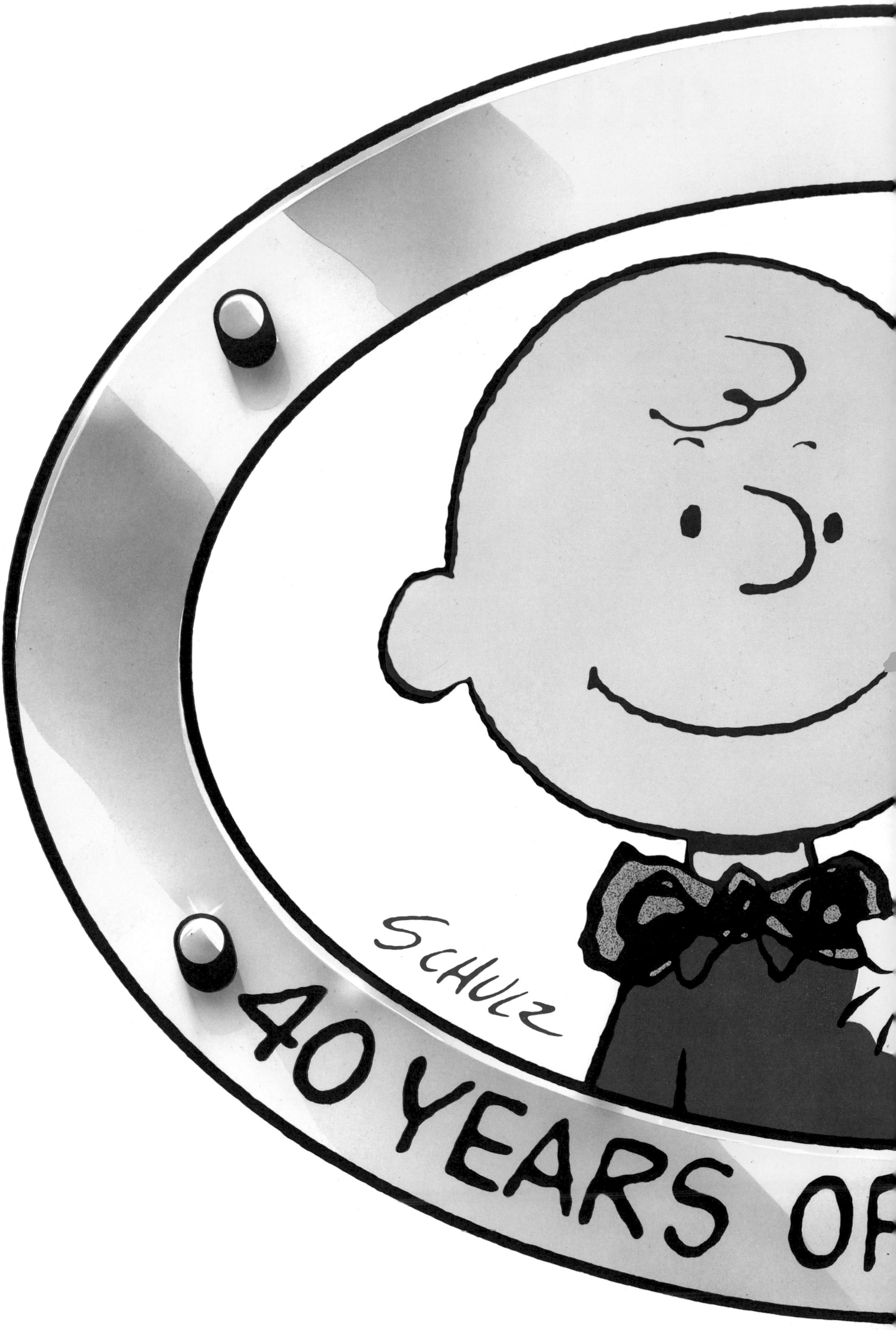
SCHULZ
40 YEARS OF

HAPPINESS

PEANUTS Characters: © 1950, 1958, 1965 United Feature Syndicate, Inc.

Peppermint Patty's End-of-Term Test

At the end of term, Peppermint Patty was given a general knowledge test at school. She did manage to complete the paper before dropping off to sleep, but she still scored the dreaded D-Minus. When you read her answers, you'll see why . . .

1. Who designed St Paul's Cathedral in London?

Christopher Robin

2. What is an 'oboe'?

An oboe is a tramp in America.

3. For what is Penzance famous?

Pirates.

4. Who was Robin Hood?

He was a man dressed up in red cape who took food to his sick grandmother in Sherwood Forest.

5. Can you complete this sentence by providing the missing word:
'Ben ....is the highest mountain in Scotland.'

Elton

6. What is a 'vandal'?

A vandal is a sort of open-toed shoe you wear in the summer.

7. What is the Matterhorn ?

It's something to do with mountains. I think it's a big horn you blow when there's something the matter.

8. What is coal made of?

Coal is made of fallen trees and decayed vegetarians.

9. Can you name the famous inlet on which the city of Edinburgh stands?

It doesn't stand on an inlet; it stands on dry land! (I think the inlet's called The Firth of Froth.)

10. Correct this sentence:
'It was me what spilt the milk.'

It wasn't me what spilt the milk!

I ♥ BASEBALL

11. Who was Macbeth?

Macbeth was the horse belonging to Dick Turpin, the highwayman.

12. What is a 'molecule'.

A molecule is a funny little round eyeglass that mad professors put in one of their eyes.

13. With what do you connect the name, Sir Arthur Conan-Doyle?

That's easy! A hyphen!

14. What is a 'reef'?

A reef is a circle of flowers you send to a funeral.

15. What do you understand by the term 'irrigation'.

It's when something keeps annoying you, like an itch or a fly.

16. Describe 'hysterics'.

Hysterics are special sloping letter you use when you want to emphasise something.

17. Do you know the meaning of the Latin phrase 'Nota Bene'?

I think it means broke, or penniless.

18. If you were in Harlem, where would you be?

Somewhere in Turkey. It's a place where Sultans keep all their wives.

19. Write a sentence with the word 'litre' in it.

The dog next-door has just had a litre of puppies

20. What is an 'inhibition'.

An inhibition is just like an exhibition, except that it is held indoors.

PP 4 CHUCK

35

ALIAS SNOOPY

A beagle in his time plays many parts! Here are 10 pictures of Snoopy in some of his most famous roles. Can you say what they are?

1.

2.

3.

4.

5.

6.

7.

8.

9.

10.

CHOP
CHOP
CHOP
CHOP

THE SEVENTIES

ALL-TIME RECORD-BREAKER

At the 1972 Olympic Games, American swimmer, Mark Spitz, won a staggering total of 7 gold medals. It is a world record which still stands today.

MONEY, MONEY, MONEY

In 1971, Britain switched to decimal currency. Instead of 240 pennies to the pound, there were now 100. Despite being much more logical, many people found the 'new money' hard to understand.

Discotheques (a French word meaning 'record library') started in the 50s, became fashionable in the 60s and universally popular in the 70s. John Travolta set new standards of disco dancing with his energetic performance in the film 'Saturday Night Fever.'

Picturepoint – London

Picturepoint – London

The first Jumbo Jet went into service in 1970. Able to carry over 350 passengers, the Boeing 747 heralded a new era of cheap air-travel for all.

Picturepoint – London

After the mini-skirt came hot pants which were really just fashionable shorts. Other 70s fashion-trends were the maxi-dress and platform shoes.

SUMMER OF '76

1976 will always be remembered as the year of the incredibly hot summer. Weeks and weeks of soaring temperatures caused sales of ice-cream and soft drinks to rocket, but the heatwave also led to water-shortages in many parts of the UK.

BIBLE BEST-SELLER

A new translation of the Bible (The New English Bible) went on sale in 1970. Demand for it was so great that it sold a million copies in just one day.

Picturepoint – London

Skateboarding was the main craze of the decade. Originating in America in the late 60s, it swept Britain and Europe in the mid-70s.

PEANUTS

I HATE HAVING SO MANY FAULTS...

I'D REALLY LIKE TO BE A BETTER PERSON

I WONDER WHAT IT WOULD BE LIKE TO KNOW THAT YOU WERE PERFECT?

TAKE IT FROM ME, IT'S A GREAT FEELING!

1971

PEANUTS

YOU'RE REALLY SOMETHING, DO YOU KNOW THAT?

I'VE NEVER SEEN ANYONE WHO WAS SO UPTIGHT ABOUT SCHOOL!

WHY DON'T YOU JUST RELAX?

WHO CAN RELAX?

PEANUTS
featuring
"Good ol' Charlie Brown"
by Schulz

THERE ARE TEN MILLIMETERS IN ONE CENTIMETER...ONE HUNDRED CENTIMETERS IN ONE METER AND ONE THOUSAND METERS IN ONE KILOMETER...

11-17

I CAN'T REMEMBER ALL THAT! WHAT ARE THEY TRYING TO DO TO US?!

I JUST GOT INCHES AND FEET FIGURED OUT, MARCIE... NOW, THEY THROW METRICS AT US! I'LL GO CRAZY!

YOU'LL CATCH ON BEFORE YOU KNOW IT, SIR...

SOMEBODY'S ALWAYS TRYING TO CHANGE THINGS!

IT'S THOSE PEOPLE ON THE SCHOOL BOARD! THEY ALWAYS GET CARRIED AWAY...

GIVE THEM A MILLIMETER AND THEY TAKE A KILOMETER!

SEE? YOU'RE CATCHING ON, SIR!

1975

PEANUTS
featuring
"Good ol' Charlie Brown"
by SCHULZ

GOOD GRIEF! THAT HOME IS RIGHT IN THE NEXT BLOCK!

I HAVE A SUGGESTION TO MAKE..

RATS!

WE'VE HAD SOME BURGLARIES IN OUR NEIGHBORHOOD LATELY...

I DON'T THINK YOU CAN GUARD OUR HOME PROPERLY FROM UP THERE...

MY SUGGESTION IS THAT YOU SIT HERE BY THE FRONT DOOR TONIGHT

I MIGHT ALSO SUGGEST THAT YOU GET YOURSELF SOME KIND OF WEAPON...

2-6

SCHULZ

RING!

HELLO? OH, HI! NO, NOTHING MUCH...

JUST SITTING HERE WATCHING THE LOWER HALF OF A MOVIE!

5-3 © 1979 United Feature Syndicate, Inc.

GOOD EVENING, SIR... WILL YOU BE DINING ALONE, SIR?

OUR SPECIAL TONIGHT IS DOG FOOD! WOULD YOU CARE TO SEE OUR WINE LIST? NO? VERY WELL...

5-4

YOUR WAITER WILL BE WITH YOU IN A MOMENT... ENJOY YOUR MEAL..

I HATE IT WHEN HE'S IN A GOOD MOOD

1979

LISTEN TO ME, YOU STUPID BEAGLE

TELL YOUR STUPID FRIEND THAT IF HE WAKES ME UP AGAIN AT FIVE IN THE MORNING WITH HIS STUPID CHIRPING, I'M GONNA PUNCH HIS STUPID BEAK!

5-10

© 1979 United Feature Syndicate, Inc.

HOW'S YOUR NOON CHIRPING?

MAYBE YOUR SONGS AREN'T HAPPY ENOUGH

AFTER ALL, IT'S SPRING!

5-7

SING SOMETHING THAT MAKES PEOPLE HAPPY...

COLOURFUL KITES

Charlie Brown loves kites, but he never succeeds in getting one to fly properly. He usually ends up looking like this, a victim of the notorious 'kite-eating tree'.

Other people have been more successful at getting their creations airbourne and kites have a long and colourful history. This is their story. . .

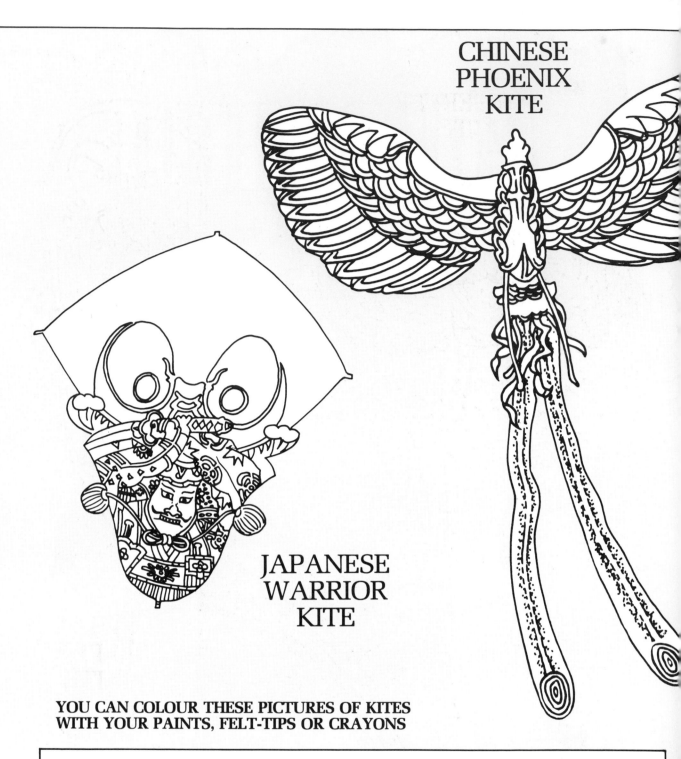

CHINESE PHOENIX KITE

JAPANESE WARRIOR KITE

YOU CAN COLOUR THESE PICTURES OF KITES WITH YOUR PAINTS, FELT-TIPS OR CRAYONS

Kites are named after the kite hawk, a bird of prey which hovers high above the ground searching for food . . . kites were first flown by the ancient Chinese and Japanese, although the Greeks claim that the idea was invented by the scientist, Archytas of Tarentum, in the fifth century BC . . . the Romans also flew kites which often had little bells attached to them, but the pastime of kite-flying did not become popular amongst British children until as late as Shakespeare's time . . . the most famous kite-flyer of all time was Benjamin Franklin, the American scientist, inventor and diplomat. In 1752, he flew a kite in a thunderstorm with a key suspended from it. The key gave off a spark, proving that lightning is

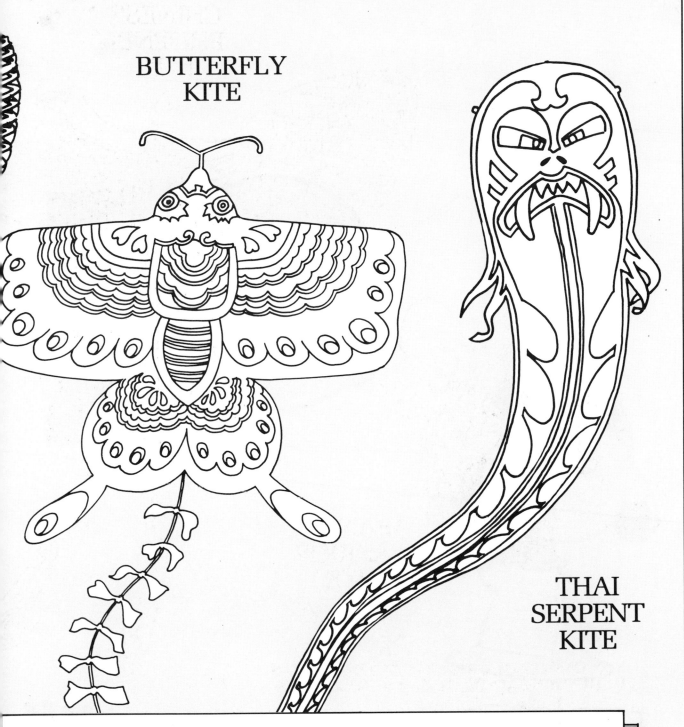

BUTTERFLY KITE

THAI SERPENT KITE

electricity. (This experiment should never be repeated as many who copied Franklin were injured by shocks) . . . kites come in all shapes and sizes, but they fall into three main categories — the malay kite (diamond-shaped, like Charlie Brown's); the three-stick kite (hexagonal), and the box-kite (rectangular-shaped, invented in the 1890s by an Australian, Lawrence Hargrave) . . . the largest kite ever flown measured 19 metres by 14 metres (approx 62×46 feet) and weighed about 300kg (660lb). It flew in Japan in 1980 and needed 500 people to hold the strings . . . the longest kite-flight in history lasted 169 hours (just over 7 days) by a team of American Kite-flying enthusiasts in 1977.

IT'S NO FUN PLAYING HIDE-AND-SEEK WHEN NO-ONE COMES TO LOOK FOR YOU!

I'M ENTITLED TO MY OPINION AND YOU'RE ENTITLED TO MY OPINION!

IF A PICTURE'S WORTH A THOUSAND WORDS, MUSIC'S WORTH A MILLION!

'IT'S BETTER TO GIVE THAN RECEIVE' IS CERTAINLY TRUE OF ADVICE!

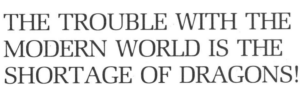

THE TROUBLE WITH THE MODERN WORLD IS THE SHORTAGE OF DRAGONS!

A BEST FRIEND IS SOMEONE WHO TELLS YOU WHAT YOU WANT TO HEAR AND WHAT YOU DON'T WANT TO HEAR!

THE EIGHTIES

Picturepoint – London

1981 was the year of the Royal Wedding. On July 29th, Prince Charles married Lady Diana Spencer in St Paul's Cathedral. The ceremony was watched by 700 million television viewers around the world.

BIKE CRAZE

BMX bikes were the biggest craze of the 80s. These rugged bikes with thick tyres could be ridden anywhere (BMX actually stands for 'bicycle motocross') and used to perform stunts.

HALLEY'S COMET

Halley's Comet was clearly visible in 1986. It won't be seen again for another 75 years.

Television soap-opera reached new heights of popularity during this decade. Leading the field was 'Dallas' with the infamous JR played by Larry Hagman.

Picturepoint – London

POP PHENOMENON

Live Aid, one of the greatest pop concerts ever held, took place in 1985. Organised by Bob Geldof, the two simultaneous concerts in Britain and America raised £40 million for desperately needed famine-relief in Africa.

THE MARY ROSE

The wreck of the Tudor galleon, Mary Rose, was raised from the bed of the Solent in 1982. The ship is now on display in Portsmouth.

Picturepoint – London

Torvill and Dean, the British ice-dancers, won Olympic gold medals in 1984. Skating to the music of Ravel's Bolero, their stunning performance gained maximum marks for artistic impression.

Picturepoint – London

In 1985, 17-year-old Boris Becker became the youngest player to win the men's singles championship at Wimbledon. Earlier in the decade, Swedish player Bjorn Borg also made tennis history by winning the title for five years running.

YOU DIDN'T SEND MY SISTER A VALENTINE... YOU BROKE HER HEART..

TECHNICALLY, I SHOULD PUNCH YOU IN THE NOSE!

I HOPE YOU DON'T

YOU'D PROBABLY MISS, AND HIT ME IN THE EYE!

WHAT COULD I DO, CHARLIE BROWN? YOUR SISTER FOLLOWS ME AROUND CALLING ME HER "SWEET BABBOO"

I NEVER SAID I WAS GOING TO GIVE HER A VALENTINE! IT WAS ALL IN HER IMAGINATION!

SO IF YOU STILL WANT TO PUNCH ME IN THE NOSE, GO RIGHT AHEAD!

WHY DON'T I JUST HOLD MY FIST OUT, AND THEN YOU WALK INTO IT?

1983

I FEEL GRUMPY TODAY.. I DON'T WANT TO TALK TO ANYBODY OR SEE ANYBODY!

I'LL HOLD MY FIST OUT, LINUS, AND YOU WALK INTO IT...

GET OUT OF MY WAY!

BONK!

DID IT HURT?

NO, BUT IT MIGHT LATER IF WE STICK AROUND

WHAT HAPPENED?

YOU HIT ME, YOU BLOCKHEAD!

I DIDN'T HIT YOU...YOU RAN INTO MY FIST

WHAT WAS YOUR FIST DOING IN THE MIDDLE OF THE SIDEWALK?

IF YOUR BROTHER HAD GIVEN MY SISTER A VALENTINE, THIS NEVER WOULD HAVE HAPPENED...

THAT'S RIGHT! IT WAS MY SWEET BABBOO'S FAULT!

I'M NOT YOUR SWEET BABBOO!

Dear Victoria,
My name is Spike.

I live alone in the desert.

Please send me your photograph. I will add it to my collection.

1-11

"AND THEN HE WAS HOME AT LAST WITH HIS FAITHFUL DOG ASLEEP AT HIS FEET"

SEE? SOME DOGS SLEEP AT THE FEET OF THEIR MASTERS...

Z

1-24

1984

IF WE WERE MARRIED, I'D FIX YOUR COLD CEREAL FOR YOU EVERY MORNING...

AND THEN YOU'D PROBABLY TALK THE WHOLE TIME SO I COULDN'T EAT, AND THE CEREAL WOULD GET SOGGY

1-27

OUR MARRIAGE IS IN DEEP TROUBLE..

THEY SAY IT MAY SNOW AGAIN TONIGHT

I JUST THOUGHT YOU MIGHT LIKE TO BE PREPARED...

1-28

HIPPITY-HOP

**BUNNIES HIPPITY-HOP...
DOGS DON'T HIPPITY-HOP..**

1-21

DOGS ARE LUCKY...

**DOGS NEVER HAVE
TO DO HOMEWORK..**

**DOGS NEVER REALLY
HAVE TO DO ANYTHING**

**JUST LISTEN TO
CRITICISM ...**

1-23

1985

TWENTY-SEVEN..

**THE AVERAGE PERSON
MOVES IN HIS OR HER
SLEEP THIRTY TIMES
A NIGHT...**

TWENTY-EIGHT...

TWO MORE TO GO..

1-24

**" DEAR SNOOPY,
WE'VE HAD SOME
COLD MORNINGS HERE
ON THE DESERT "**

**" TODAY I ACTUALLY
HAD A FIRE IN MY
FIREPLACE "**

1-26

FIREPLACE ?

Panel 1: I WISH THE SCHOOL BUS HADN'T COME..

Panel 2: IT'S GOING TO RUIN MY NOON

Panel 3: HOW CAN A SCHOOL BUS RUIN YOUR NOON?

Panel 4: I LEFT MY LUNCH BOX SITTING ON THE CURB!

Panel 1: YES, MA'AM, I LEFT MY LUNCH BOX ON THE CURB BY THE BUS STOP...

Panel 2: SOMEONE'S PROBABLY FOUND IT BY NOW

Panel 3: I JUST HOPE WHOEVER FOUND IT APPRECIATES A GOOD LUNCH...

Panel 4: NO DOUGHNUTS !?!

1986

Panel 1: THIS IS MY REPORT ON THE "KILLER BEES"

Panel 2: MANY PEOPLE ARE WORRIED ABOUT THE "KILLER BEES"

Panel 3: NOT ME

Panel 4: WHAT I WORRY ABOUT ARE THOSE "KILLER D-MINUSES"!

Panel 1: I'M TIRED OF BEING WISHY-WASHY! I'M GONNA WALK RIGHT OVER, AND TALK TO THAT LITTLE RED-HAIRED GIRL!

Panel 2: I'M DOING IT! I'M COMMITTED! NOTHING CAN STOP ME NOW!

Panel 3: ABSOLUTELY NOTHING!

Peppermint Patty's

Project

Peppermint Patty was feeling fed-up. Snoopy spotted her sitting on her front doorstep with a miserable expression on her face. So he scampered over and put one paw on her knee, as if to ask: "What's wrong?" Patty gave him a brief smile. "I'm aching to try out my new baseball bat, Snoopy," she explained, "but I have to do some schoolwork first. Because I did so badly in my end-of-term test, I've been given some extra homework. It's hard, too – I can't do it!"

Snoopy spotted Patty's school file on the ground beside her. He picked it up and looked at it. "Perhaps I can help," he thought. It was an English project. Patty had seven questions to answer, but she had only managed the first one. It said:

'Explain the meaning of the word 'CLICHÉ'.'

Patty had written:

' 'CLICHÉ' is a word used in fencing. When you touch your opponent with your sword, you shout "CLICHÉ" to show that you have won the match.'

Snoopy rolled his eyes in dismay. "Oh, dear!" he thought.

Snoopy knew all about clichés. Having used them himself for many years while writing his great, unfinished novel, he was quite an expert on them. So he hurried back to his kennel and put Peppermint Patty's piece of file paper in his typewriter. Then he typed the correct answer:

'A 'CLICHÉ' is a phrase or saying that is used so much it becomes boring and tedious to read.'

Hopping down from his kennel, Snoopy returned the paper to his friend.

Patty was very grateful to have one question answered correctly. "What about the other questions, Snoopy?" she cried. "I can't even answer them at all!" Snoopy took the paper back. "Let the brainy beagle have another look," he thought.

TRY TO COMPLETE THESE WELL-KNOWN SAYINGS:

2. ONE GOOD TURN DESERVES – – – – – – –.

3. – – – – – – – – – MAKES PERFECT.

4. IT'S AN ILL WIND THAT BLOWS – – – – – –
– – – – – – –. (3 words)

5. A – – – – – – – IN NEED IS A – – – – – – INDEED.

6. NO TIME LIKE – – – – – – – – – –. (2 words)

7. THERE'S NO PLACE LIKE – – – –.

Snoopy could not
answer the questions, either.
Can YOU do them?

Seeing the disappointed look on Patty's face, Snoopy nipped back to his typewriter and wrote her a note. It said:

"Would you care to accompany me to the library? We can look up these sayings in a book."

"Great idea, Snoopy!" cried Patty, leaping to her feet. "Let's get going!"

Snoopy and Patty had not gone far down the road when they met Charlie Brown. He was on his way to the park. "Hey, you two," he called, excitedly, "I've had a great idea! I'm not going to fly my kite – it always ends in disaster! I'm going to fly this paper plane instead!"

The two friends watched as Charlie Brown launched his plane into the air. "It flies beautifully!"

he cheered, running after it. The paper dart sped across the park and disappeared over a fence into someone's back garden. "Now I've lost it!" wailed Charlie Brown. There was a hole at the bottom of the fence, so Snoopy squeezed through and fetched the paper plane back. Charlie Brown was thrilled. He fished in his pocket and brought out some chocolate-chip cookies which he gave to Snoopy. "One good turn deserve another." he said. "Aha!" though Snoopy.

Just then, Lucy came along. She was wobbling about on a pair of roller skates. "You don't look very safe on those," commented Charlie Brown. "I'm better at roller-skating than you are, Charlie Brown!" retorted Lucy. "In fact, I'm better than anyone else in our neighbourhood. I'm one of the best roller-skaters in the world!"

To prove it, Lucy sped off down the path. "Mind that tree," thought Snoopy. "See, Charlie Brown," called Lucy, turning round, "pretty good, eh?" BLAM! Lucy collided with the tree! Snoopy and his pals could not help laughing. "Okay, okay!" yelled Lucy, getting up and dusting herself down. "So I made a mistake! Well, practice makes perfect!" "Aha!" thought Patty.

Lucy skated off in a huff and Charlie Brown went on flying his plane. Then Snoopy spotted Linus approaching, carrying a box of sweets. Before Patty could stop him, the sweet-toothed beagle had bounded over and was sitting on his hind legs, begging imploringly. "No, Snoopy," said Linus, firmly, "these are NOT for you!" "Meanie!" thought Snoopy.

Linus marched off down the path. Suddenly, Lucy came hurtling round the corner on her roller skates. "Look, Snoopy," she whooped, "I've really got the hang of it now!" THUD! Lucy bumped into Linus, sending him sprawling. His sweets flew out of their box and rolled in front of Snoopy who instantly gobbled them up. He slunk away, expecting Linus to be cross, but Lucy's younger brother just sat on the grass, looking amused. "Oh, well," he said, philosophically, "it's an ill wind that blows nobody any good." "Interesting," thought Snoopy.

Snoopy and Patty continued on their way. They were soon distracted, however, by the sound of sweet music drifting across the park. Schroeder was playing his piano in a nearby bandstand! Snoopy closed his eyes and let the music of Beethoven wash over him. Suddenly, though, the concert stopped! "Rats!" snorted Schroeder. Opening his eyes, Snoopy saw that the lid of Schroeder's toy piano had blown open. "The catch is broken," explained the young pianist. "Every time the wind blows, it flies up." So Snoopy jumped up and sat on Schroeder's piano, keeping the lid in place. "Thanks, pal," laughed Schroeder, "a friend in need is a friend indeed." "What did he say?" murmured Peppermint Patty.

When the concert was over, Snoopy jumped down from the bandstand and rejoined Patty. She was talking to Sally who had arrived with her brother's American football. "Charlie Brown has never managed to kick this," she told them, "so I'm going to have a try." Snoopy could see his master still flying his paper plane, and he knew he would be cross that his ball had been borrowed. So Snoopy tugged Sally's sleeve and pointed urgently across the park. "Thanks, Snoopy," said Sally. "I'll get kicking right away. No time like the present!"

BOOT!

Sally gave the ball a hefty boot. It flew over her head, bounced in several different directions and then hit Sally in the small of her back, knocking her over. "Perhaps it's a good thing the round-headed kid has never managed to kick that ball!" thought Snoopy.

Suddenly, Patty glanced at her watch. "Come on, Snoopy," she called, "we must get a move on or the library will be closed!" The two friends hurried out of the park and made their way down the road. As they rounded the street-corner, however, a strange figure hurried past them, carrying a cactus "That's Spike!" thought Snoopy.

Snoopy raced after his brother and tapped him on the shoulder. Spike put the cactus down. "Hello, Snoopy," he said. Snoopy asked him where he was going. "Back to the desert," replied Spike. "I've been to visit our sister, Belle, but I don't like it in the city. Too noisy and crowded." Snoopy invited Spike to stay with him for a few days, but Spike shook his head. "I want to get back to Needles," he explained, "there's no place like home!"

Snoopy watched his brother disappearing in the distance, then raced after Patty who had continued on to the library. He found her sitting on the steps outside, looking miserable again. "It's closed!" she sighed. Snoopy looked at her and winked. Then he nudged her elbow. Slowly, the dawn of realisation came into Patty's eyes. "Of course!" she grinned, getting to her feet. "We don't need the library, do we? We know the answers now!"

Their adventures on the way had given the answers to all 6 questions. Patty wrote them down on a piece of paper she fished out of her pocket. "Hurray!" cheered Patty. "My project's finished!

Did YOU spot the answers hidden in the story? If not, here they are:
2. ONE GOOD TURN DESERVES ANOTHER.
3. PRACTICE MAKES PERFECT.
4. IT'S AN ILL WIND THAT BLOWS NOBODY ANY GOOD.
5. A FRIEND IN NEED IS A FRIEND INDEED.
6. NO TIME LIKE THE PRESENT.
7. THERE'S NO PLACE LIKE HOME.

Now Patty was free to play baseball. She collected her shiny new bat and hurried down to the park. "Get your team together, Charlie Brown," she called. "We've just got time for a game before it gets dark."

Charlie Brown caught the ball that Patty threw to him and got ready to pitch. Snoopy joined Lucy and the others who stood around the park, waiting to field. Then Peppermint Patty stepped up to the batting square, her bat poised to whack the ball into the pale blue yonder. "Want to know my favourite saying?" she chuckled. "EVERYBODY'S GOOD AT SOMETHING!"